ALESSANDRO SANNA

YOU BRING THE FURNITURE

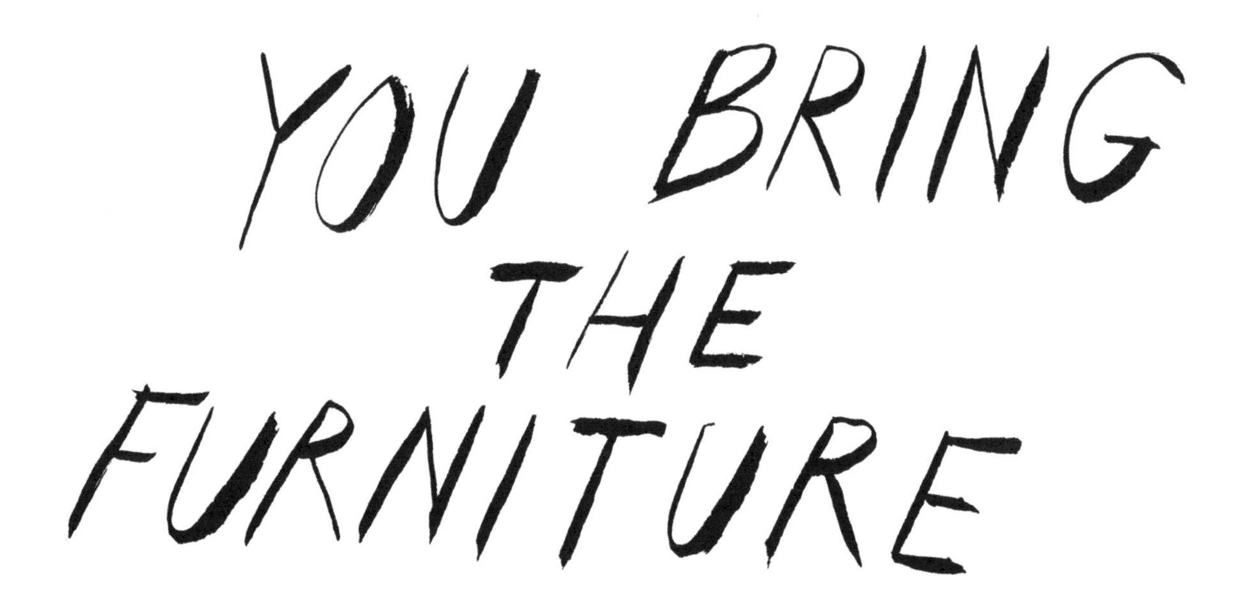

EDIZIONI CORRAINI

Come in.

I'm coming with the tea.

Here I come!

Ooooooh!!!

Whoops, sorry.

Perhaps I'll make some lemonade.

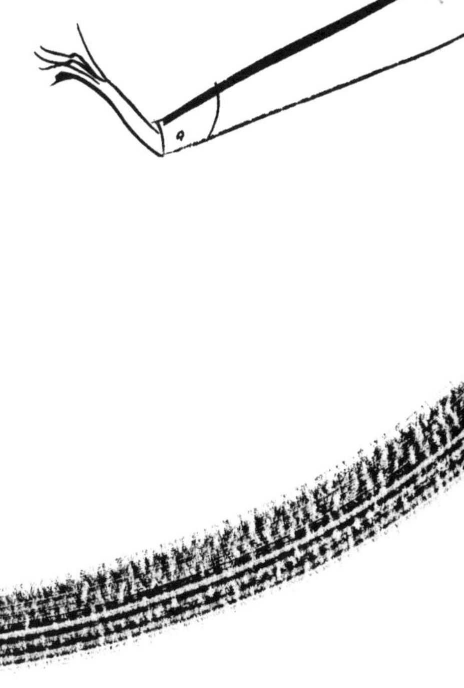

les grands trans-Parents

Is it sour?

Then I'll give you a saw, a hammer and a nail and you can turn your furniture into Ultramobili!

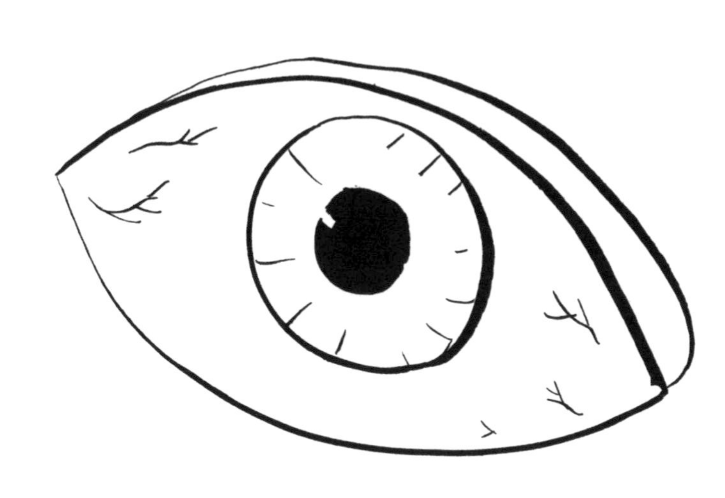

LES GRANDS TRANS-PARENTS

MAN RAY

1938/1971

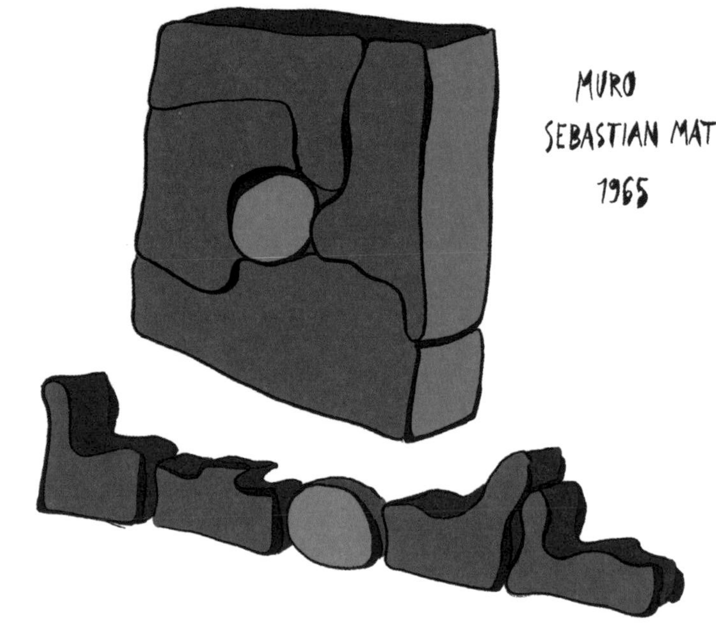

MURO

SEBASTIAN MATTA

1965

COSTANTIN

STUDIO SIMON, HOMMAGE TO COSTANTIN BRANCUSI

1980

FAUSTO

NOVELLO FINOTTI

1972

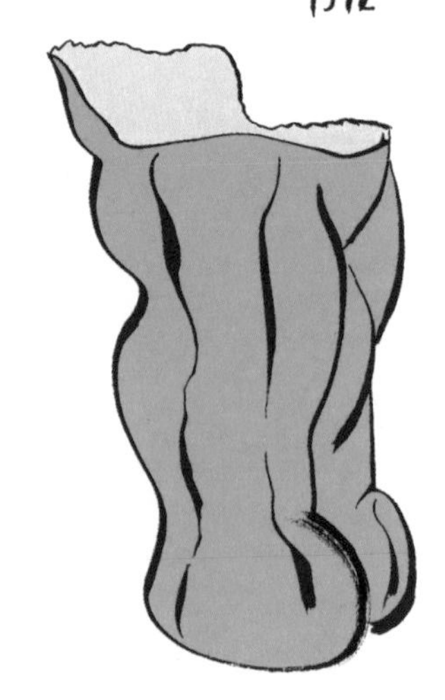

MAGRITTA

SEBASTIAN MATTA

1971

MARGARITA
SEBASTIAN MATTA
1970

PARAVENTO BALLA
GIACOMO BALLA
1917/1971

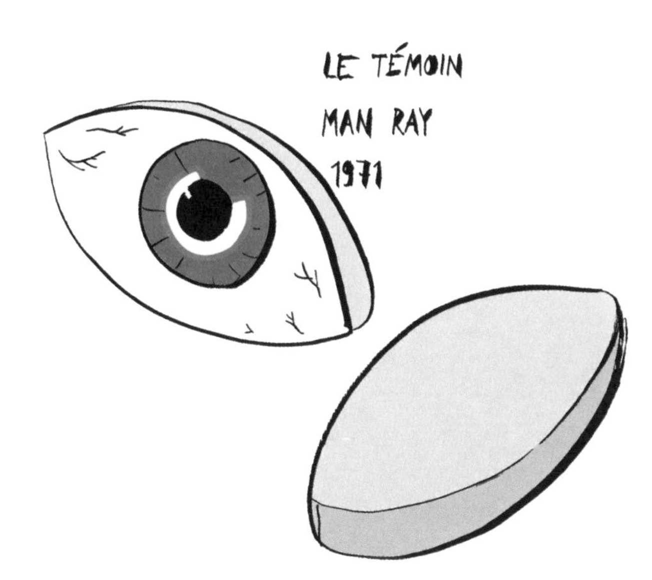

LE TÉMOIN
MAN RAY
1971

TRACCIA
MERET OPPENHEIM
1939/1972

RON RON
MARION BARUCH
1972

"Ultramobile" are works of art in the shape of furniture.
Designed by international artists they are conceived to bring objects into the home whose presence is poetic and full of life... one step beyond the functionality and rationality of design. Introduced by Dino Gavina in 1971 as part of an operation that combined both art and entrepreneurship, many of the Ultramobili are still being produced.

Alessandro Sanna
You bring the forniture

Printed to coincide with the exhibition
"Dino Gavina. Lampi di design", MAMbo.
Bologna 23 September - 12 December 2010

Translated by Isobel Butters

Printed in Italy by PubliPaolini, Mantova
September 2010

Maurizio Corraini s.r.l.
via Ippolito Nievo, 7/A
46100 Mantova
tel. 0039 0376 322753
fax 0039 0376 365566
e-mail: sito@corraini.com
www.corraini.com